FOURT

ASSESSMENT

REASONING

JM BOND

Nelson

Thomas Nelson and Sons Ltd
Nelson House Mayfield Road
Walton-on-Thames Surrey KT12 5PL   UK

51 York Place   Edinburgh   EH1 3JD   UK

Thomas Nelson (Hong Kong) Ltd
Toppan Building 10/F   22A Westlands Road
Quarry Bay   Hong Kong

Thomas Nelson Australia
102 Dodds Street South Melbourne
Victoria 3205 Australia

Nelson Canada
1120 Birchmount Road Scarborough
Ontario M1K 5G4 Canada

© **J M Bond 1977, 1983, 1986, 1994**

First published by Thomas Nelson and Sons Ltd 1977
Second edition 1983
Revised edition 1987
This fully revised edition 1994

Pupil's Book ISBN 0-17-424517-3
              NPN 9 8 7 6 5 4 3 2 1
Answer Book ISBN 0-17-424518-1
              NPN 9 8 7 6 5 4 3 2 1

. **By the same author**
First, Second, Third, Fourth and Further Fourth Year
Assessment Papers in Mathematics

First, Second, Third, Fourth and Further Fourth Year
Assessment Papers in English

First, Second, Third and Further Fourth Year
Assessment Papers in Reasoning

Filmset in Nelson Teaching Alphabet
by Mould Type Foundry Ltd
Dunkirk Lane Leyland Preston England

Printed in England
by Ebenezer Baylis & Son Ltd
The Trinity Press Worcester and London

Paper 1

In this code shapes are used in place of letters. Here are four words and underneath them are four sets of shapes, but they are not beneath the right words. Can you sort them out?

b a l l	b a d	b e d	b a l e
□ ☉ ◇	□ ○ △ △	□ ○ △ ☉	□ ○ ◇

1 **ball** should be □○△△

2 **bad** should be □☉◇

3 **bed** should be □○◇

4 **bale** should be □○△☉

Put these words into the code.

5 deal ....

6 ebb ....

7 dale ....

8 lead ....

9 add ....

10 bleed ....

11 What is the fifth odd number greater than 21? ....

12 Which number is exactly half-way between 39 and 63? ....

Fill in the missing word in each of the following lines.

13	busy/bee	quiet/mouse	blind/...............
14	strong/horse	slow/snail	meek/...............
15	sharp/needle	sweet/honey	right/...............
16	white/snow	green/grass	brown/...............
17	good/gold	clean/new pin	fit/...............
18	black/coal	thick/thieves	tough/...............

There are five vowels: **a**, **e**, **i**, **o** and **u**.

19–21 Underline any of the words below which contain all these vowels.

platinum   favourite   peculiar   pineapple
equatorial   affectionate   mosquito   cauliflower

22 If you wrote all the numbers from 19 to 30 how many times would you write the figure **2**? ....

Fill in the next two numbers or sets of letters in each of the lines below.

23–24	de	gh	jk	mn	....	....
25–26	ab	ef	ij	mn	....	....
27–28	7	8	10	13	....	....

Underline the right word in the brackets.

29 Man is to woman as boy is to (child, baby, girl, lady)
30 Bee is to hive as spider is to (net, web, nest, barn)
31 Pig is to sty as snail is to (garden, soil, slug, shell)
32 Seven is to seventy as hundred is to (million, ten, seven, thousand)
33 One is to first as two is to (double, second, third, first)
34 Good is to better as bad is to (best, worst, better, worse)
35 What is the smallest number which, when divided by 4, 6 or 8, has a remainder of 3? ....
36 Take the next even number greater than 88 from the next odd number smaller than 101. ....

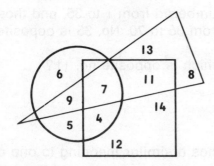

37 Find the sum of the numbers in the triangle, but not in the square. Take this number from the sum of the numbers in the square, but not in the circle. ....
38 Add together the numbers in the triangle, but not in the circle. Take from this number the sum of the numbers in the circle only. ....
39 Find the sum of the numbers in the square, but not in the triangle. Take from this number the sum of the numbers in the triangle only. ....

The words on each of these lines follow a pattern. Look at them carefully, and then write the next word on each line.

40 heir   her   lady   lay   pain   ....
41 sloth   lot   eager   age   power   ....
42 smooth   moot   brides   ride   change   ....
43 stork   rot   dwarf   raw   snipe   ....
44 delay   ale   stiff   fit   storm   ....
45 silent   sent   minute   mute   palace   ....

Three years ago John was five years old, and his mother was five times his age.

46 How old will his mother be in four years' time? ....
47 How old will John be then? ....

5

48 Which letter appears most frequently in the word **accommodation**?

....

Underline the word in each line which has a completely different meaning from the other words.

49	pain	discomfort	aid	suffering	distress
50	discover	detect	reveal	cover	find
51	cause	error	mistake	fault	flaw
52	tie	loosen	unite	fasten	join
53	end	finish	source	completion	conclusion
54	tutor	trainer	instructor	teacher	pupil

The houses on one side of the road are numbered from 1 to 35, and those on the other side of the road are numbered from 36 to 70. No. 35 is opposite to no. 36.

55 What is the number of the house which is opposite no. 11?
No. ....

56 No. 23 is opposite no. ....

57 No. 31 is opposite no. ....

On each line one of the words on the left has a similar meaning to one of the words on the right. Underline both words.

58–59 ruler, strict, bent   straight, severe, sentence

60–61 second, minute, hour   tiny, time, clock

62–63 busy, thankful, lenient   lazy, merciful, tired

Put the following words in the order in which you would find them in the dictionary.

autumn   annual   ancient   August   aunt   adult

64 (1) ....   **65** (2) ....   **66** (3) ....

67 (4) ....   **68** (5) ....   **69** (6) ....

Can you sort out these jumbled words?

Vegetable soup

70 1 sliced **nonoi** ....

71 1 sliced **totopa** ....

72 1 sliced **pinurt** ....

73 1 sliced **rocart** ....

74 2 sticks of **yelerc** ....

75 1 sprig of **slaryep** ....

76 1 pint of **tocks** ....

77 1 pinch of **slat** ....

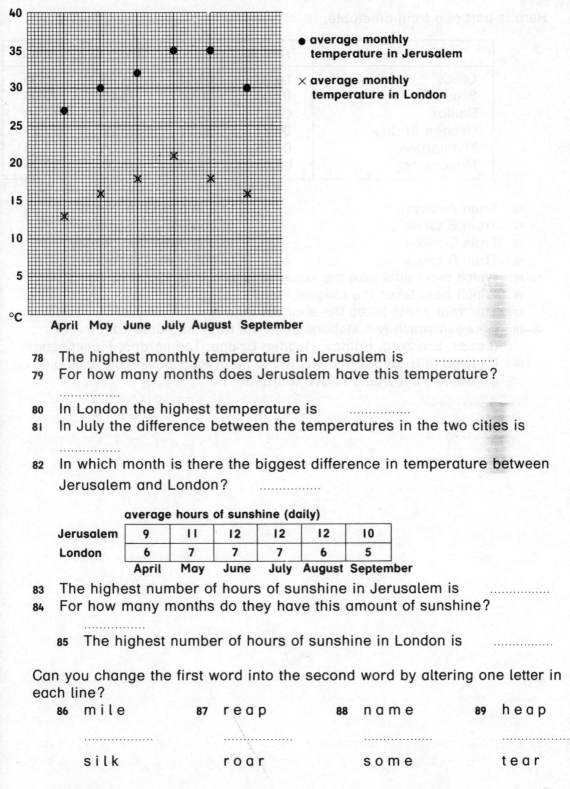

40
35
30
25
20
I5
I0
5
°C

● average monthly
temperature in Jerusalem

× average monthly
temperature in London

April May June July August September

78 The highest monthly temperature in Jerusalem is ....
79 For how many months does Jerusalem have this temperature?
....
80 In London the highest temperature is ....
81 In July the difference between the temperatures in the two cities is
....
82 In which month is there the biggest difference in temperature between
Jerusalem and London? ....

	average hours of sunshine (daily)					
Jerusalem	9	II	12	12	12	10
London	6	7	7	7	6	5
	April	May	June	July	August	September

83 The highest number of hours of sunshine in Jerusalem is ....
84 For how many months do they have this amount of sunshine?
....

85 The highest number of hours of sunshine in London is ....

Can you change the first word into the second word by altering one letter in
each line?

86 m i l e   **87** r e a p   **88** n a m e   **89** h e a p

....

s i l k   r o a r   s o m e   t e a r

7

Here is part of a train timetable.

	Train A	Train B	Train C	Train D
Leeds	06.35	09.35	14.35	16.35
Bradford	07.00	10.00	15.00	17.00
Halifax	07.13	10.13	15.13	17.13
Hebden Bridge	07.27	10.27	15.27	17.27
Todmorden	07.35	10.35	15.35	17.35
Manchester	08.06	11.03	16.07	18.06

90 Train A takes .... to complete the journey.
91 Train B takes .... to complete the journey.
92 Train C takes .... to complete the journey.
93 Train D takes .... to complete the journey
94-95 Which two trains take the same time to do the journey? ....
96 Which train takes the longest time? ....
97 The train which takes the shortest time is ....
98-99 Between which two stations does the travelling time vary?
       (Leeds, Bradford, Halifax, Hebden Bridge, Todmorden, Manchester)
100 If I lived in Bradford and wished to be in Manchester by 10.00 a.m.
     on which train would I have to travel? ....

Underline one number in each of the three brackets to make the sum correct.

1–3   (7, 2, 4) × (3, 5, 2) = (18, 16, 12)

4–6   (9, 18, 12) ÷ (3, 4, 2) = (2, 5, 9)

Tom and Paul learn Latin and French. Paul and Tim learn French and Spanish. John and Tom learn German and Latin.

7   Who learns Latin but not French? ....

8   Who learns French but not Spanish? ....

9   Which language does Tom not learn? ....

10   Who learns German but not French? ....

11   Which language does Paul not learn? ....

12   Who learns Latin, French and Spanish? ....

Underline one word from each set of words in brackets to give the right answer.

13–14   Foot is to person as (mane, hoof, saddle) is to (cat, rider, horse)

15–16   Person is to house as (fish, animal, bird) is to (sea, nest, scales)

17–18   Hand is to clock as (poetry, spoke, lesson) is to (wheel, speak, verse)

19   A man went to the bank to cash a cheque. He was given new £5 notes which were numbered consecutively from 449276 to 449373. How much money did he get? ....

20   If Sunday is the first day of the week what are the middle letters of the fifth day of the week? ....

On each line there are two words which have opposite meanings. Underline both words.

21–22   blue   colour   pale   green   dark   tint

23–24   feeble   fertile   harvest   autumn   season   barren

25–26   cheap   expansive   cost   expensive   price   common

Fill in the letter which will best finish the first word and also start the second word.

27   deb .... rod

28   the .... any

29   cas .... nee

30   fas .... hin

31   hal .... ish

32   Which letter occurs twice in **transparent**, once in **wretched** and not at all in **insolent**? ....

33-39 Mrs. X goes to the bank to cash a cheque for £7·78. She asks if she can receive the smallest number of notes and coins possible.
She receives:

.... £5 notes
.... £1 coins
.... 50p coins
.... 20p coins
.... 10p coins
.... 5p coins
.... 2p coins
.... 1p coins

There is one word on each line which cannot be formed from the letters of the word on the left (using each letter once only). Underline that word.

40	**reduction**	notice	direct	deduct	toured	ironed
41	**description**	potion	prone	prince	credit	notice
42	**character**	archer	earth	crater	charter	teacher
43	**purchases**	shares	cheeps	spruce	arches	sharp
44	**concentrate**	trace	concrete	contents	accent	trance
45	**atmosphere**	heroes	phrase	stream	spread	master

On each line three pairs of words have similar meanings, but one pair have opposite meanings. Underline that pair.

46	regret/sorrow	option/choice	host/guest	feeble/weak
47	doctor/patient	test/try	glance/look	coarse/rough
48	terror/fear	moan/groan	sleek/smooth	speak/listen
49	withdraw/retire	accuse/blame	curb/control	guilt/innocence
50	accept/refuse	divide/share	inquire/ask	transparent/clear
51	vanquish/defeat	extend/enlarge	deluge/drought	custom/habit

The following are times of trains between Appleton and Bakewell. Fill in the missing figures in the chart.

		Leaves Appleton	Journey lasts	Arrives at Bakewell
52	Train A	09.53	.... minutes	10.28
53	Train B	10.17	45 minutes	....
54	Train C	11.49	42 minutes	....
55	Train D	12.19	.... minutes	13.12

56 Which is the fastest train?   ....
57 Which is the slowest?   ....

Fill in the missing figures in these sums.

58–60
```
  3 6....
  2....9
+ ....7 8
───────
  1 1 9 4
```

61–64
```
  6....1 3
– 1 4 5....
─────────
  ....5....6
```

65–68
```
  5....9....
×       6
───────
  3....7....4
```

69–70
```
      1 5 7....
  5 ) 7....9 5
```

Here are some long words, and, on the right of the page, some shorter words which have the same meaning. They are not in the right order. Can you sort them out?

71 **enigma** means ....   mock
72 **opulent** means ....   underground
73 **elliptical** means ....   oval
74 **immaculate** means ....   sitting
75 **colossal** means ....   puzzle
76 **indolent** means ....   rich
77 **subterranean** means ....   huge
78 **deride** means ....   lazy
79 **sedentary** means ....   spotless

diction   action   notion   emotion

If these four words are spelled backwards and then put into alphabetical order, which will be:

80 the first?   ....
81 the last?   ....

meant   tent   consent   comment

If these four words are spelled backwards and then put into alphabetical order, which will be:

82 the second?   ....
83 the third?   ....

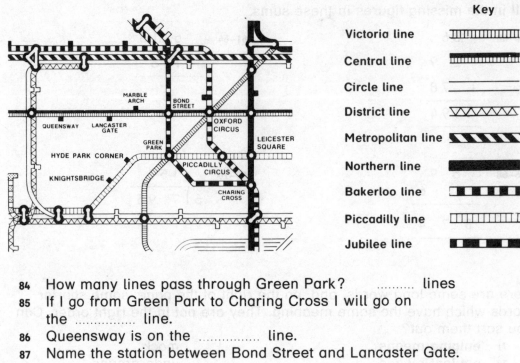

Key

Victoria line	
Central line	
Circle line	
District line	
Metropolitan line	
Northern line	
Bakerloo line	
Piccadilly line	
Jubilee line	

84 How many lines pass through Green Park? .... lines

85 If I go from Green Park to Charing Cross I will go on the .... line.

86 Queensway is on the .... line.

87 Name the station between Bond Street and Lancaster Gate.

....

See how quickly you can do these:

88 248 × 50

....

89 306 × 50

....

90 188 × 50

....

91 232 × 50

....

In a certain code the word **surgeon** is written **4783652**. In this code:

92 **3526** is ....

93 **5784** is ....

94 **8546** is ....

95 **85376** is ....

96 **4552** is ....

97 **27846** is ....

98 If I had 7 more books I would have half as many as Charles. I have 15. How many has Charles? .... books

99 In two years time I will be three times as old as my brother who is 2. How old am I now? .... years

100 When I am 13 he will be .... years

Paper 3

One word is different in some way from the other words in the line.
Underline that word.

1	sword	pistol	spear	dagger	lance
2	hen	duck	goose	cow	bull
3	team	captain	gang	horde	herd
4	cub	puppy	sow	fawn	calf
5	grunts	croaks	purrs	gallops	bellows
6	less	latest	best	least	most

7 Which letter is in **paint** but not in **pantry**? ....
8 Which letter is in **principle** but not in **principal**? ....
9 Which letter is in **pedestal** but not in **pedestrian**? ....
10 Which letter is in **response** but not in **resonance**? ....
11 Which letter is in **peculiar** but not in **pecuniary**? ....
12 Which letter is in **contingent** but not in **continue**? ....

13–17 Underline the words in which three vowels appear next to each other.

agreeable   believe   luscious   heinous   bureau
radius   eloquence   ingenuous   beetroot   piteous

A concert was held on three days: February 27th, 28th and 29th.

18 In which year was the concert?   (1990, 1992, 1994, 1996)
19 Two days after tomorrow is Saturday. Which day was the day before yesterday? ....
20 If the months were put in alphabetical order, which would be the last month? ....
21 Which would be the 6th month? ....
22 If the days were put in alphabetical order which would be the first day? ....
23–24 Counting Sunday as the first day of the week, which days have the same position alphabetically as they have in the week?
....

Underline the pair of words which have opposite meanings.

25	whole/total	increase/enlarge	heal/hurt
26	obey/command	earn/gain	map/plan
27	busy/alert	dear/expensive	common/rare
28	consent/dissent	omen/sign	frank/candid
29	excess/surplus	entrance/exit	famous/renowned

Underline the word which rhymes with the word on the left.

30	**rough**	cough	cuff	laugh	how	through
31	**dough**	through	bough	enough	foe	tough
32	**bawl**	trail	bail	wool	sale	fall
33	**heir**	here	fur	dare	ear	weir
34	**tier**	fear	heir	fare	fire	sir

What relation is:

35 Mrs. Andrews to her son's daughter? ....

36 Mrs. Bell to her father's brother? ....

37 Mrs. Collins to her sister's brother? ....

38 Tom to his father's mother? ....

39 Jane to her brother's wife? ....

Underline one word from each section in brackets to make a sensible sentence.

40–42 (Steven, Anne, the baby) found the (rattle, dog, book) in her (desk, hut, bottle).

43–45 (Seven, four, ten) plus (six, eight, five) equals (nine, eleven, fourteen).

46–48 (Thames, Pacific, London) is a (city, lake, ocean) in (Scotland, England, France).

49–51 A (dog, rose, oak) is a (tree, bush, flower) which blooms in (winter, summer, spring).

52–54 The (postman, gardener, grocer) (dug, delivered, drove) the (counter, flower, letter).

In each space write the missing number.

55	18	13	9	6	....	3
56	60	48	38	....	24	20
57	3	8	14	21	29	....
58	....	12	18	25	31	38
59	11	13	12	15	....	17

Arrange these famous people in order of age by numbering them in the brackets. Put the eldest first.

60	Elton John	born 1947	....
61	Andrew Lloyd Webber	born 1948	....
62	Barbra Streisand	born 1942	....
63	Kylie Minogue	born 1968	....
64	Cliff Richard	born 1940	....
65	Michael Jackson	born 1958	....

House of Hanover	Reign
George I	1714–1727
George II	1727–1760
George III	1760–1820
George IV	1820–1830
William IV	1830–1837
Victoria	1837–1901

66 For how many years did these kings and queens reign altogether?
....

67 Who was on the throne at the end of the nineteenth century?
....

68 Who was on the throne at the end of the eighteenth century?
....

69 Napoleon died in 1821. In whose reign was this? ....

70 The Battle of Trafalgar was in 1805. Who was reigning then?
....

71 Sir Christopher Wren died in 1723. How long had George I been king?
....

72 Which monarch reigned for the shortest time? ....

73 Victoria was 18 when she came to the throne. Who was king when she was born? ....

Here is a chart which shows the cost of some holidays to Tunisia.

Departure date between	7 nights	14 nights
23 June – 6 July	£280.00	£360.00
7 July – 16 July	£290.00	£370.00
17 July – 22 July	£320.00	£400.00
23 July – 9 Aug	£340.00	£420.00

74 A 2 week holiday starting on June 23rd will cost ....

75 What would be the cost for 2 people to have a week's holiday starting on July 17th? ....

76 Find the cost for one person to have 2 weeks' holiday starting on July 10th. ....

77 How much would a family of 3 people save by having 2 weeks' holiday starting on July 7th instead of waiting until July 17th? ....

78 How much more does it cost to stay for 2 weeks rather than 1 week? ....

Here is part of a train timetable.

	Chester	Euston	
Train A	**07.18**	**10.00**	
Train B	09.10	11.54	
Train C	**10.28**	**13.14**	SO A
Train D	11.10	14.10	
Train E	**14.38**	**17.23**	SX
Train F	15.15	18.03	

Heavy type denotes "through"
trains; otherwise trains stop at
Crewe.
SO   Saturdays only
SX   Mondays to Fridays
A   May to September

79   Which is the first train to stop at Crewe?   ....
80   Train .... doesn't run on Saturdays.
81   Which of these trains runs only in the summer?   ....
82   Does Train F stop at Crewe?   ....
83   How many "through" trains are shown on the timetable?   ....
84   How many trains are there any day in the winter?   ....

The words on each of the following lines follow a pattern. Can you fill in the missing word?

85	bird	bride	part	prate	cart	crate	salt	....
86	write	wit	tread	tea	stone	son	speak	....
87	cheap	cap	avoid	aid	bread	bad	plain	....
88	clear	arc	loyal	all	abuse	sea	anger	....
89	what	hate	shop	hope	glut	lute	drop	....

Find a letter which will finish the first word and also start the second word.

90   hal .... ish
91   als .... nce
92   sol .... ven
93   mic .... ach

94   Which number is exactly half-way between 44 and 80?   ....

English numbers: 1 2 3 4 5 6 7 8 9

Egyptian numbers: I ϒ ≺ Ɛ O ⁊ V Λ 9

95–96 Which Egyptian numbers look rather like some of our numbers but do not have the same value? ....

97–98 Which Egyptian numbers are like ours and have the same value? ....

99 Which Egyptian number is like the Roman numeral 5? ....

100 Which Egyptian number is a mirror reflection of one of ours? ....

Below are some proverbs. On each line the letters of one of the words have been jumbled up. In the space write the word as it should be spelled.

1 A **gnllior** stone gathers no moss. ....

2 Beggars can't be **serchoos**. ....

3 Don't count your **skinecch** before they are hatched. ....

4 **hengou** is as good as a feast. ....

5 Exchange is no **royberb**. ....

6 Familiarity breeds **tentcomp**. ....

7 Fine **eheatsfr** make fine birds. ....

8–10 Jane has a £15.00 book token. Here are some of the books she would like to buy. Which books does she get if she spends £15.00 exactly?

A Schoolgirls' Annual   £9.95
B Show Jumping manual   £4.50
C Pocket Book of Birds   £1.55
D James and the Giant Peach   £2.95
E Standard Dictionary   £3.50

Jane bought ....

One word or number is, in some way, different from the others on the line. Underline it.

11	oak	ash	beech	pine	elm
12	daffodil	primrose	violet	tulip	catkin
13	83	63	33	36	18
14	49	56	79	28	63
15	chair	stool	bench	form	table
16	church	hall	chapel	cathedral	abbey

The words on each line follow a pattern. Look for it and then complete each line.

17	sword	words	spick	picks	stuck	....
18	steam	seam	steal	seal	brass	....
19	motor	rot	straw	war	order	....
20	garnet	ant	wearer	err	circle	....
21	friend	red	assist	sit	admire	....
22	centre	ten	create	are	please	....

Underline the smallest and put a ring round the largest number on each line.

23–24	413 250	413 025	413 205	423 125	423 521
25–26	87 659	87 679	87 695	86 796	86 759
27–28	31 205	32 150	31 250	32 105	32 125

a b c d e f g h i j k l m n o p q r s t u v w x y z

Arrange the letters of the alphabet so that the vowels are first, followed by the consonants.

29 Which is now the tenth letter? ....
30 Which is now the twenty-first letter? ....
31 How many letters are in the same place in this alphabet as they are in the proper alphabet? ....
32 In which place is letter **b**? ....
33 Which letter is just before **b**? ....
34 How many letters are there between **h** and **p**? ....

Choose one of the words from the column on the right of the page to best fill each space.

35 The match .... in a draw.   rescued
36 The best seats were .... for the parents.   restored
37 The lady .... at Holt Hall.   resulted
38 The lifeboat .... the sailors.   resigned
39 The headmaster was .... by all the village.   resided
40 The traffic was .... to one side of the road. reserved
41 The craftsman .... the old table.   respected
42 The teacher .... at the end of the term.   restricted

Underline the two words on each line which have similar meanings.

43–44	famous	name	person	renowned	rich
45–46	lure	fear	power	dread	firm
47–48	cause	cross	disorder	choose	pick

The first word in each line can be changed into the second word in three stages, by altering one letter at a time. Can you fill in the first two stages?

49–50	take	....	....	live
51–52	pipe	....	....	hill
53–54	good	....	....	work
55–56	home	....	....	ripe

In Roman numerals **V = 5, X = 10, L = 50.**

57	XXVIII	=	....	58	XLII	=	....	
								59 XXIV = ...
60	XXXIX	=	....	61	LI	=	....	62 LXXV = ...

63 Which letter appears once in **matinee**, twice in **dungeon** and three times in **pronunciation**? ....

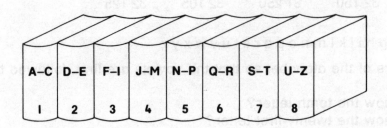

A–C	D–E	F–I	J–M	N–P	Q–R	S–T	U–Z
1	2	3	4	5	6	7	8

Here is a set of encyclopaedias.

In which volumes would you find details of the following?

   64 Parliament   Volume ....

   65 Kings of England Volume ....

   66 Bees   Volume ....

   67 Saints   Volume ....

   68 Diamonds   Volume ....

   69 Owls   Volume ....

   70 Gold   Volume ....

   71 West Indies   Volume ....

Here are some mapping signs.

   wood   **park**   **heathland**

   quarry   **open pit**   **orchard**

Draw each sign in the correct square:

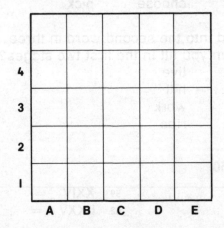

   72 a wood in C4

   73 a quarry in B1

   74 a park in E3

   75 an orchard in A4

   76 heathland in D2

   77 an open pit in A2

To multiply by 25, you add two noughts and then divide by 4.

Example: 40 × 25 = 4000 ÷ 4 = 1000

78   36 × 25   79   44 × 25

    ....

80   64 × 25   81   48 × 25

    ....

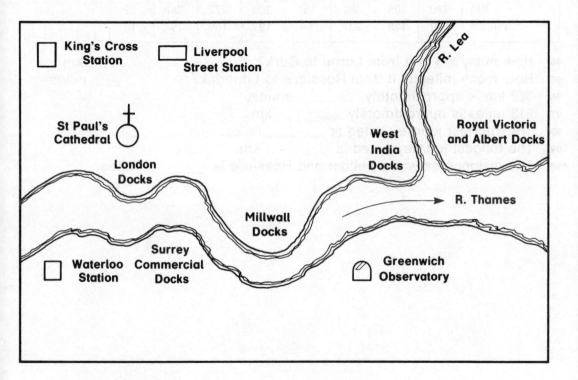

82   In which direction does the River Thames flow?   ....
83   Is St. Paul's Cathedral north or south of the river?   ....
84   How many stations are north of the Thames?   ....
85   How many stations are south of the Thames?   ....
86   How many docks are on the south bank of the river?   ....
87   How many are on the north bank?   ....
88   Greenwich Observatory is (N, S, E, W) of the West India Docks.

89–93   I owe Timothy 87p. I want to repay him with as few coins as possible. How can I do this?

     .... 50p .... 20p .... 10p .... 5p 2p

21

IRELAND	Belfast	Cork	Donegal	Dublin	Limerick	Killarney	Galway	Wexford
LARNE								
KM	40	461	184	206	359	469	342	340
MILES	25	287	115	128	223	292	213	211
ROSSLARE								
KM	320	205	382	151	205	272	268	19
MILES	199	128	237	94	127	169	197	12

94 How many km is it from Larne to Cork? .... km

95 How many miles is it from Rosslare to Limerick? .... miles

96 382 km is approximately ....miles.

97 213 miles is approximately .... km.

98 The shortest journey listed is .... miles.

99 The longest journey listed is .... km.

100 The distance between Belfast and Rosslare is .... miles.

Paper 5

Complete the following table:

	Train leaves at	Journey lasts	Train arrives at
1	09.37	....	10.21
2	10.41	38 minutes	....
3	....	51 minutes	12.05
4	12.27	....	13.02
5	13.29	47 minutes	....
6	....	1 hour 9 minutes	15.05

Find a word which could be put in front of the other words on the line to form a compound word or a pair of words that go together.

7	boat	buoy	guard	jacket	....
8	way	proof	pistol	mark	....
9	guard	man	escape	drill	....
10	cutter	lark	pecker	worm	....

Put the following words in alphabetical order.

stripe　　　string　　　stripling　　　strike　　　strip　　　stringent

11	(1)	12	(2)	13	(3) ....
14	(4)	15	(5)	16	(6) ....

Underline the item which is the second largest in each group.

17	chapter	word	paragraph	letter	sentence
18	thousand	million	one	hundred	ten
19	hour	week	second	day	minute
20	most	few	more	least	some
21	town	county	street	country	village
22	68	135	89	210	23
23	cat	cow	mouse	sheep	dog

One word on each line cannot be formed from the letters of the word on the left (using each letter once only). Underline it.

24	**instalment**	stint	stain	meat	later	last
25	**stratagem**	stage	magnet	stream	master	treats
26	**promised**	prised	drips	spread	prose	drop
27	**residence**	nicer	inside	creed	scene	denser
28	**permanent**	tramp	preen	meant	parent	natter
29	**miserable**	blame	sable	blear	table	miles
30	**pleasantly**	antler	pleat	slant	steal	peasant

Underline one number in each set of brackets to make each sum correct.

31–33 (18, 20, 19) + (11, 14, 12) = (28, 35, 33)

34–36 (8, 6, 7) × (5, 9, 7) = (64, 63, 60)

37–41 Underline any word in which one letter appears exactly twice and another letter appears three times.

buccaneer	photographer	hippopotamus	follower
memorandum	embezzle	conscience	possession
swallow	eccentric	dependent	grasshopper

42 Which vowel appears once in **teach** and twice in **assemble**? ....

43 How many letters appear twice in **occasionally**? ....

44 Which letter in **indigenous** is nearest the beginning of the alphabet? ....

45 Which letter in **extravagance** is nearest the end of the alphabet? ....

46 How many different letters are there in **rhododendron**? ....

Two of the pairs of words on each line have opposite meanings. One pair are not related in that way. Underline that pair.

47 proper/improper   tidy/untidy   take/mistake

48 valuable/invaluable   kind/unkind   popular/unpopular

49 audible/inaudible   possible/impossible   sent/dissent

50 known/unknown   patch/dispatch   own/disown

51 miss/dismiss   opened/unopened   usual/unusual

52 press/impress   agree/disagree   fasten/unfasten

53 disconnect/connect   sane/insane   verse/converse

In each space write the missing letters or numbers.

54	az	by	cx	....	ev	fu
55	bd	bf	bh	....	bl	bn
56	pon	rqp	tsr	....	xwv	zyx
57	dbc	fde	hfg	....	ljk	nlm
58	bz	ey	hx	....	nv	qu
59	b2d	c3e	d4f	....	f6h	g7i

60 Tim had a jigsaw which had 300 pieces. It took him $2\frac{1}{2}$ hours to complete it. What was the average number of pieces he put in per minute? ....

61 If the alphabet was divided in the middle into 2 equal parts, how many vowels would there be in the first half? ....

62 How many consonants would there be in the second half of the alphabet? ....

24

Underline the word which rhymes with the word on the left.

63	**forfeit**	feat	fate	lit	forget
64	**laid**	late	weighed	said	side
65	**wide**	width	widow	beside	height
66	**receipt**	recipe	receive	conscript	feat
67	**believe**	weave	belief	leaf	live
68	**calm**	firm	turn	harm	ham
69	**yacht**	catch	fetch	pat	hot
70	**persuade**	said	fade	head	lead

What must the word on the left have?

71	car	(garage, engine, radio, clock)
72	river	(boats, fish, water, bridge)
73	school	(chalk, blackboards, desks, pupils)
74	garden	(grass, hedge, soil, tree)
75	chair	(cover, arms, seat, cushion)
76	house	(chimneys, roof, furniture, curtains)
77	piano	(stool, locks, keys, music)

Andrew and Mark together had 18 sweets. Mark and Chris together had 22 sweets. Together the three boys had 30 sweets.

78–80   Andrew had ...., Mark had .... and Chris ....

81   How many sweets must Chris give Andrew if they are all to have the same number of sweets? ....

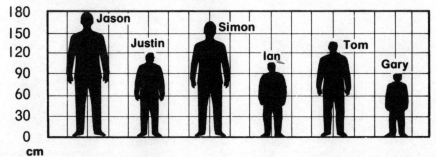

Look at this graph which shows the heights of some boys. Calculate the scale to which it is drawn, and then give the height of each boy.

82   Jason is .... cm

83   Ian is .... cm

84   Justin is .... cm

85   Tom is .... cm

86   Simon is .... cm

87   Gary is .... cm

88   How much taller is Jason than Ian? ....

89   Simon is .... cm taller than Tom.

90   How much shorter is Gary than Ian? ....

In a certain code, **stream** is written 145327. In the same code, what would these numbers represent?

91 7214 ....
92 254 ....
93 7324 ....
94 3241 ....
95 5314 ....
96 45331 ....
97 721435 ....

3 rubbers and 2 ballpoints cost £1.15
4 rubbers and 2 ballpoints cost £1.40

98 1 rubber costs ....
99 1 ballpoint costs ....

100 What is the smallest number which, when divided by 2, 3 or 4, has a remainder of 1? ....

Paper 6

On each line there are two words which have similar meanings. Underline both the words.

1-2   contract   conspire   expand   convince   enlarge
3-4   sometimes   frequently   never   often   ever
5-6   expensive   price   cheap   costly   money
7-8   fire   smoke   cook   heat   conflagration

One number in each line is incorrect. Underline it, and then write the correct number in the space at the end of the line.

9   100   81   64   48   36   25   ....
10   49   58   66   76   85   ....
11   941   852   763   674   586   ....
12   7   15   25   31   43   51   61   ....

Sort out these jumbled questions, and then answer them at the end of the line.

13   opposite is what the accept the word of?   ....
14   goat what is called young of a the?   ....
15   patron is who Wales saint of the?   ....
16   comes Thursday and which Tuesday between day?   ....

Choose a word from the column on the right of the page to complete each of these expressions.

17   To look for a .... in a haystack   dogs
18   Make .... while the sun shines   needle
19   Let sleeping .... lie   goose
20   A cock and .... story   gander
21   A wild .... chase   hay
22   What is sauce for the goose is sauce for the ....   bull

23   Write the letters of the word **ostrich** in the order in which they appear in the dictionary.   ....
24   Which letter appears twice in **immigrant**, once in **prime** and not at all in **melancholy**?   ....

Put the following words in alphabetical order.

     douse   double   down   dove   doubt   dough   dour

25   Which would be the middle word?   ....
26   The last word?   ....
27   The second word?   ....

28 I put my watch right at 9 a.m. today. If it loses I minute every three hours what time will it show at 9 p.m. tomorrow? ....

29 If you wrote the numbers I to 100 how many times would you use the figure 5? ....

Use a word from the column on the right of the page to complete each line.

30 The woman, who was badly ...., was unable to stand up.

31 The clock, which had ...., needed rewinding.

32 The girl, who ran downstairs, ... over the stool.

33 The flowers, which hadn't been ...., were drooping sadly.

34 The clothes, which had been .... by the wind, were quite dry.

35 The vase, which had .... over, was smashed to pieces.

36 The man, who walked slowly, ... the bus.

37 The boy, who had long legs, ... over the gate easily.

jumped
watered
fallen
blown
missed
injured
tripped
stopped

Complete the following.

38 A s..........re has four sides.

39 He cycled to school in a few m..........tes.

40 We followed the rec..........e in making the cake.

41 There was a se..........h for the escaped prisoner.

42 The sh..........p is a very small fish.

43 My c..........in is the daughter of my aunt.

44 A br..........h is part of a tree.

The words on each line follow a pattern. Look for it and then complete each line.

45	hare	hear	hate	heat	feel	....
46	lose	sole	sent	nest	went	....
47	tales	stale	anger	range	trips	....
48	saloon	son	modern	men	diving	....
49	stream	mart	velour	rule	draper	....
50	gambol	goal	carrot	coat	magnet	....
51	threw	wet	tapes	set	groan	....

52 Underline the middle word in order of speed.

marched   crawled   ran   walked   sauntered

28

Choose from the column on the right of the page a word which is associated with a word on the left.

53	rough and	only
54	all and ....,.....	tumble
55	time and	go
56	rack and	sundry
57	one and	tongs
58	hammer and	again
59	touch and	ruin
60	over and	over

61 How many letters are there in the alphabet before the third vowel?
....

62 How many letters are there are in the alphabet after the fifth vowel?
....

Can you sort out the jumbled words?

63–70 It was Amanda's birthday and she had asked **vlrseea** ....
friends to tea. Dad had made a lovely fruit **aadls** .... which
had **craoptis** .... , **groanes** .... and
chaspee .... in it. There was a **glear** .... cake with
veeenl .... candles on it. They enjoyed the
asasueg .... rolls most of all.

Forty children did four tests. This chart shows their marks.

Subject	Marks					
	0–29	30–44	45–54	55–64	65–74	75+
English	4	9	5	8	7	7
Mathematics	7	8	5	9	7	4
Geography	2	7	7	10	8	6
History	4	4	8	7	9	8

71 In English, how many children had fewer than 45 marks? ....
72 In Mathematics, how many had more than 64 marks? ....
73 In Geography, ... children gained between 45 and 64 marks.
74 In History, how many children had more than 54 marks? ....
75 In which subject did the most children have fewer than 45 marks?
....

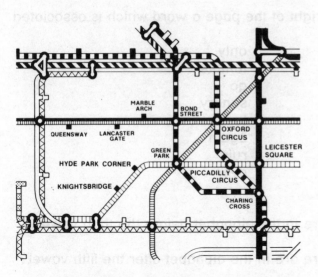

Key

Victoria line	
Central line	
Circle line	
District line	
Metropolitan line	
Northern line	
Bakerloo line	
Piccadilly line	
Jubilee line	

76 If you are at Piccadilly Circus and want to go to Hyde Park Corner you would travel on the .... line.

77 How many stations would you pass through? ....

78 Piccadilly Circus and Oxford Circus are on the .... line.

79 Piccadilly Circus is the next station to Leicester Square on the .... line.

80 Bond Street and Oxford Circus are both on the .... line.

81 88 × 25

....

82 164 × 25

....

83 288 × 25

....

84 364 × 25

....

Here is part of a chart showing distances between large cities.

	Montreal	New York
Amsterdam	5506 km	5850 km
Brussels	5555 km	5885 km
Cairo	8729 km	9017 km

85 What is the distance between Amsterdam and New York? .... km

86 Between Cairo and Montreal there is a distance of .... km

87 There are .... km between Brussels and New York.

88 There are .... km between Cairo and New York.

89 The distance between Amsterdam and Montreal is .... km

In a restaurant it is usual for 10% of the bill to be added as a service charge. What would be the service charge on these bills?

90 £8·90 ....   91 £20·50 ....
92 £11·80 ....   93 £36·60 ....
94 £12·40 ....   95 £40·40 ....

Here is part of a bus timetable.

Manchester Bus Station	09.05
Manchester Airport	09.27
Runcorn	09.55
Ellesmere Port	10.23
Chester Zoo	10.35
Chester Bus Station	10.45

96 How long does it take to travel between Manchester and Chester Bus Stations? ....

97 The shortest distance is between (Manchester Bus Station and Manchester Airport, Manchester Airport and Runcorn, Ellesmere Port and Chester Zoo, Chester Zoo and Chester Bus Station)

98 How much longer does it take to get from Manchester Bus Station to Manchester Airport, than it does to get from Chester Zoo to Chester Bus Station? ....

99 How much less than half an hour does it take to get from Runcorn to Ellesmere Port? ....

100 From Ellesmere Port to Chester Zoo is .... minutes less than $\frac{1}{4}$ hour.

On each line there are two pairs of words which are opposites. One pair are not. Underline that pair.

1	often/seldom	many/few	great/big
2	uppermost/top	quiet/noisy	minute/huge
3	buy/sell	bridge/river	profit/loss
4	yours/mine	theirs/ours	my/mine
5	time/watch	climb/descend	give/take
6	speak/listen	generous/mean	angry/cross
7	divide/multiply	throw/catch	heat/cook

Here are some words which have also been written in code. Look at them carefully because the code numbers may not be beneath the right words.

shoe	show	whose	sow	rose
5762	562	8651	5761	27651

Write what the code should be for these words.

8	shoe	....	9	whose	....
10	sow	....	11	show	....
12	rose	....			

In the same code how would these words be written?

13	shower	....	14	horror	....

On each line there are two words which are associated with the word on the left. Underline these words.

15–16	**clock**	head	hands	thumbs	face	legs
17–18	**coal**	mine	ours	your	vase	pit
19–20	**book**	attendant	page	flower	leaf	pot

Underline the correct word in each set of brackets.

21 Safe as (bells, rocks, houses, streets, horses)
22 Cool as a (ice, cucumber, velvet, water, bone)
23 Flat as a (fiddle, feather, needle, pancake, waffle)
24 Happy as a (sandboy, new pin, honey, play, baby)
25 Quick is (life, lightning, running, winking, train)
26 Clear as (glass, bell, steel, mirror, crystal)
27 Dull as (death, school, wet day, ditchwater, doorpost)

28 Write the letter which appears most often in **international**, and after it write the letter which follows it in the alphabet. ....

32

Underline the word which has the same meaning as the word on the left.

29	**replete**	replied	full	refuse	pull	repast
30	**edible**	edifice	ending	enormous	eatable	drinkable
31	**succulent**	juicy	frugal	childlike	dry	burnt
32	**derelict**	artificial	ancient	adjoining	abandoned	let
33	**indolent**	idol	lazy	lifeless	lacking	longing
34	**surmise**	guess	surmount	surround	gossip	surface
35	**monotony**	once	morsel	sameness	monument	verse

Which numbers are represented by these Roman numerals?

36 LXV = ...   37 XLIV = ...   38 LXXII = ...

Use a word which rhymes with the word on the left to complete each sentence.

39	toys	The course for the rowing event was marked with ....
40	meet	They bought a .... of furniture.
41	fire	The .... sang the school song.
42	set	She was glad to pay off the ....
43	cuff	There was a storm and the sea was very ....

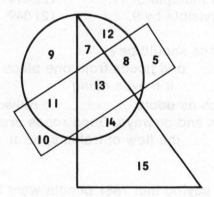

44 From the sum of the numbers in the triangle but not in the rectangle, take the sum of the numbers in the rectangle but not in the circle.

....

45 Find the sum of the numbers in the rectangle but not in the triangle, and the numbers in the circle but not in the rectangle.   ....

46 From the sum of the numbers in the circle but not in the triangle, take the sum of the numbers in the rectangle but not in the triangle.

....

Find a word which could be put in front of each of the other words on the line to make a compound word or a phrase.

47	bow	fall	proof	water	....
48	house	ship	hearted	weight	....
49	paper	foil	plate	smith	....
50	breast	Cross	Indian	Admiral	....
51	board	mail	bird	currant	....

Underline the word which has an opposite meaning to the word on the left.

52	**absent**	away	lost	out	present	gone
53	**fresh**	stale	bread	new	baked	cooked
54	**lead**	dog	collar	follow	front	van
55	**cloudy**	sky	clear	rain	mist	fog
56	**final**	end	finish	letter	post	initial
57	**verse**	rhyme	poetry	ode	prose	limerick
58	**obtuse**	angle	wide	acute	right	size

59	Put an **a** in the space by the largest of the numbers on the right of the page.	122 711	....
60	Put a **b** in the space by the smallest number.	121 446	....
61	Put a **c** by the number which is a multiple of 5.	121 524	....
62	Put a **d** by the number which is divisible by 4.	122 455	....
63	Put an **e** by the number which is a multiple of 11.	122 474	....
64	Put an **f** by the number which is divisible by 9.	121 349	....

Can you work out what these jumbled words should be?

65–71 The movement of **leepop** .... and goods from one place to another is called **aotrnsrtp** .... It moves along recognised **stoure** .... such as **adors** ...., railways, **acalns** ...., shipping lanes and airways. Good roads are most important. To **deeps** .... the flow of traffic special motorways have been **tiulb** ....

Often we "round off" numbers. Instead of saying that 7681 people went to a match we say that there were 8000 there. This is rounding off to the nearest thousand. If a number is half-way between two other numbers we take it as being nearer the larger number.
What are these numbers to the nearest ten?

| 72 | 17 | 73 | 33 |
| | .... | | .... |

| 74 | 59 | 75 | 75 |
| | .... | | .... |

34

lighten   brighten   fatten   soften

If these four words are spelled backwards and then put into alphabetical order, which will be:

76 the second? ....

77 the third?

official   essential   comical   biblical

If these four words are spelled backwards and then put into alphabetical order, which will be:

78 the first? ....

79 the last? ....

80 68×25	81 84×25	82 288×25	83 164×25
....	....	....	....

GUARANTEED DELIVERY. GUARANTEED PRICES

CONSIGNMENT WEIGHT	PARCELFORCE 48	PARCELFORCE 24	PARCELFORCE DATAPOST	
			BY NOON	BY 10AM
UP to 10 kg	£8.20	£9.90	£13.00	£17.20
11 kg	£8.60	£10.40	£13.70	£18.00
12 kg	£9.00	£10.90	£14.40	£18.80
13 kg	£9.40	£11.40	£15.10	£19.60
14 kg	£9.80	£11.90	£15.80	£20.40
15 kg	£10.20	£12.40	£16.50	£21.20
16 kg	£10.60	£12.90	£17.20	£22.00
17 kg	£11.00	£13.40	£17.90	£22.80

84 A 14 kg parcel delivered next day would cost ....

85 A parcel weighing 12.5 kg delivered in 2 days would cost ....

86 A 16 kg parcel delivered by 10 a.m. would cost ....

87 A parcel weighing 11.75 kg delivered by noon costs ....

88 A 12 kg parcel delivered by 10 a.m. costs ....

89 A parcel weighing 16.5 kg delivered in 2 days would cost ....

Here is a list of some big cities and their populations. Number them according to size starting with the largest.

90	Liverpool	528 000	....
91	London	6 970 000	....
92	Birmingham	1 041 000	....
93	Leeds	729 000	....
94	Glasgow	809 000	....
95	Sheffield	544 000	....

This chart shows certain facts about the climate in Hawaii.

	Average day temperature	Average hours of sunshine (daily)	Average monthly rainfall
April	25°C	9·0	290 mm
May	27°C	9·3	216 mm
June	28°C	9·5	170 mm
July	29°C	10·0	244 mm
August	29°C	9·0	270 mm
September	29°C	8·5	254 mm

96 Which month has the lowest temperature? ....

97 .... has the most sunshine.

98 .... has the most rain.

99 If you could go there for a holiday the best month to go would be

....

100 The worst month would be ....

Paper 8

Complete the following proverbs by writing a word from the column on the right in each space.

1 A cat may look at a ....   sleeping
2 Too many .... spoil the broth.   vessels
3 .... makes the heart grow fonder.   stitch
4 Empty .... make the most noise.   cooks
5 Let .... dogs lie.   king
6 Jack of all trades, ... of none.   absence
7 A .... in time saves nine.   master

8 When I added 2 to a number it was then half of a half of 12. What is the number? ....
9 Which letter of the word **parcel** has the same place in the alphabet as it does in the word? ....
10 If the letters of the word **fatigue** were put in alphabetical order which would be the middle letter? ....

Underline the word on each line which cannot be formed from the word on the left, using each letter once only.

11 **defendant**   deaf   fended   defeat   defer   faded
12 **distribute**   tribes   striped   brides   trust   utter
13 **considerate**   trace   creed   crate   tread   inside
14 **partridge**   trip   pride   greed   drear   drape
15 **carpenter**   creep   trace   enact   crate   tender
16 **serendipity**   pride   endorse   trends   spirit   density
17 **prosperity**   sport   proper   spite   trot   spire

Underline the word in each line which is the "odd one out".

18 tumbler   urn   vase   glass   purse
19 inside   border   edge   rim   fringe
20 stable   tent   nest   sty   den
21 hero   monk   nun   lord   earl
22 leaps   roars   bounds   runs   swings

Emma's birthday is on March 29th. Lucy's birthday is 5 days after Emma's, and Peter's is 4 weeks before Emma's.

23 Lucy's birthday is on ....
24 Peter's is on ....

Complete the following expressions by underlining one word in each set of brackets.

25 A wet (washing, blanket, sheet, cloth, dog)
26 All (whole, ends, heads, ears, noses)
27 Good for (something, appearances, nothing, evil, work)
28 Blow one's own (nose, wind, recorder, balloon, trumpet)
29 Turn over a new (job, flower, leaf, book, page)
30 Send to (London, Timbuktu, Jericho, Coventry, Wales)
31 Wait till the (hens, traffic, cars, bills, cows) come home.

BBCI broadcasts non-stop from 6 a.m. on Monday until 12.05 a.m. on Tuesday.

32 How many hours and minutes is this? ....

The first word in each line can be changed into the second word in three stages, by altering one letter at a time. Fill in the gaps.

33–34 cope .... host
35–36 hire .... torn
37–38 hair .... land
39–40 stop .... item
41–42 stow .... blob

Use a word which rhymes with the word on the left to complete each sentence.

43 sum After playing in the snow Peter's hands were ....
44 mile The .... of her dress was very modern.
45 so The baker shaped the .... into loaves.

Choose the right word from the list on the right to complete each sentence.

46 A place where weapons are stored is an .... tariff
47 The frame of a car is the .... dialogue
48 Inside a nut is the .... infantry
49 A conversation between two people is a .... chancel
50 Duty paid on exports and imports is a .... arsenal
51 Goods found floating after a shipwreck are .... kernel
52 A list of articles is an .... chassis
53 Instructions for preparing food are a .... flotsam
54 The eastern end of a church is the .... inventory
55 Foot soldiers are .... recipe

Underline any of the following flower names which have an equal number of vowels and consonants.

56–57 dandelion geranium carnation rose tulip

38

Sir Walter Raleigh	1552–1618
Admiral Benbow	1653–1702
Lord Nelson	1758–1805
Sir Francis Drake	1540–1596
Sir Sidney Smith	1764–1840
Lord Effingham	1536–1624

58 Which of these admirals was born first? ....

59 Which was born the most recently? ....

60 How old was Lord Effingham when Raleigh was born? ....

61 How old was Sir Sidney Smith when Nelson died? ....

62 Which of these men had the longest life? ....

63 Which had the shortest life? ....

64 How old was Raleigh when Drake died? ....

65 Which of these men was alive on the centenary of the death of Drake? ....

66 Queen Victoria came to the throne in 1837. Which of these men was alive then? ....

Blind people use the braille alphabet which is a series of raised dots.
Here are some of the letters of the braille alphabet.

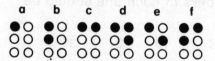

Can you read these braille words?

67 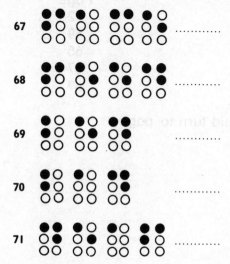 ....

68 ....

69 ....

70 ....

71 ....

39

Here is part of a train timetable.

	Train 1 SO	Train 2 FO	Train 3 SX
Coventry	14.23	15.55	16.48
Birmingham Airport	14.33	16.13	16.58
Birmingham New Street	15.11	16.48	17.22
Wolverhampton	15.28	17.06	17.47
Stafford	15.50	17.22	18.06

SO = Saturdays only
FO = Fridays only
SX = not Saturdays

72 How long does it take Train 1 to travel from Coventry to Stafford?

....

73 Train 2 takes ....
74 Train 3 takes ....
75 How many of these trains travel on Saturdays?   (1, 2, 3)
76 How many of these trains travel on Fridays?   (1, 2, 3)
77 How many of these trains travel on Wednesdays?   (1, 2, 3)

Can you work out what the next two numbers in each line should be?

78–79 $\frac{1}{2}$ $\frac{1}{4}$ $\frac{1}{8}$ $\frac{1}{16}$ $\frac{1}{32}$ ....

80–81   1   1   2   3   5   8   13   21   34   ....

The contents list to part of an encyclopaedia reads as follows:

	Page
Famous people and events	2
Explorations and discoveries	59
British Prime Ministers	65
Kings and Queens of England	67
Presidents of the U.S.A.	69

To find out about the following people I would turn to page:

82 Francis Drake ....
83 George Washington ....
84 Julius Caesar ....
85 Harold Wilson ....
86 Queen Victoria ....
87 Christopher Columbus ....
88 Horatio Nelson ....

tennis

golf

good beach

sailing

children's activities

Blue Sea Hotel

Queen's Hotel

Hotel Lido

Eden Rock Hotel

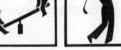

Beach Hotel

Park Hotel

This picture shows you the amenities offered in several hotels.

89 Which hotel offers tennis, golf and sailing? ....

90 How many hotels offer sailing and children's activities? (1, 2, 3, 4, 5, 6)

91 Which hotel offers golf, children's activities and a good beach?

....

92 How many offer tennis and children's activities? (1, 2, 3, 4, 5, 6)

93 How many offer golf, sailing and a good beach? (1, 2, 3, 4, 5, 6)

In each of the sets below there is one word which does not fit in with the others. Underline it:

94	emotion	95	depart	96	indiscreet
	reason		quit		reckless
	purpose		arrive		careful
	motive		leave		rash

41

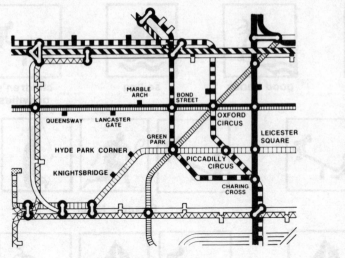

Key

Victoria line	
Central line	
Circle line	
District line	
Metropolitan line	
Northern line	
Bakerloo line	
Piccadilly line	
Jubilee line	

97 I want to go from Bond Street to Knightsbridge. They are not on the same line. Where would be the best place to change?

....

98 The first part of my journey would be on the .... line.

99 The second part of my journey would be on the .... line.

100 Name the station I would pass through on this line.

....

Paper 9

If the statement is true write **t** in the space; if it is false write **f**.

1 The equator divides the world into two equal sections. ....
2 At the beginning of British Summer Time clocks are put back one hour. ....
3 November is a longer month than March. ....
4 We live in the nineteenth century. ....
5 768 BC was earlier than 678 BC. ....
6 1990 is a leap year. ....

Find the letter which will best end the first word and start the second word.

7 gran .... aily   8 wis .... ard   9 tre .... ven
10 curv .... very   11 ter .... ice   12 bat .... ard

13–14 Smile is to happiness as (frown, tear, laugh) is to (whisper, laughter, sorrow)

15–16 Food is to hunger as (drink, water, bread) is to (eat, thirst, cold)

17–18 4 is to 1 as (2, 3, 1) is to ($\frac{1}{4}$, $\frac{3}{8}$, $\frac{5}{8}$)

Underline the correct meaning of the following expressions.

19 **To save one's face**
    To use make-up
    To avoid disgrace
    To use a sun hat
    To always do well

20 **Dead beat**
    Music without rhythm
    A dead policeman
    To take things easily
    Exhausted

21 **To throw in the towel**
    To put the towel in the washing machine
    To do a little extra work
    To clean up
    To give up

22 **To have too many irons in the fire**
    To try too many things at the same time
    To get the iron too hot
    To burn the ironing
    To take advantage of someone

Choose a word from the column on the right to complete each sentence.

23 The secretary was .... and the office was well organised.

24 The lady made a .... saying that the dress had shrunk.

25 A .... arose when they all wanted the same book.

26 It is always nice to be paid a ....

27 On .... of the work the men were paid.

28 Oxygen is a .... of water.

29 An angle of 20° is the .... of an angle of 70°.

30 Mr. Old was born in 1897 and died in 1965. How old was he when he died? ....

compliment
completion
component
complement
complication
complaint
competent

Underline the correct answer.

31 My aunt is (my sister's mother, my brother's wife, my father's sister, my daughter's mother)

32 My cousin is (my sister's child, my aunt's child, my grandmother's niece, my mother's sister)

33 My uncle is (my father's brother, my brother's son, my father's father, my brother's cousin)

34 My grandfather is (my uncle's brother, my brother's father, my father's father, my brother's uncle)

Mr. Welloff goes to the bank to cash a cheque for £99·94. He asks to be given the money in such a way that he has the smallest possible number of notes and coins.

35-41   How is he given his money?

....	£50 notes	....	50p coins
....	£20 notes	....	20p coins
....	£10 notes	....	10p coins
....	£5 notes	....	5p coins
....	£1 coins	....	2p coins
		....	1p coins

Underline the "odd one out" in each line.

42	sing	song	shout	hum	call
43	desert	leave	pursue	forsake	abandon
44	Mersey	Snowdon	Dee	Thames	Severn
45	stare	gaze	glance	hear	watch
46	tap	rap	stride	strike	knock

Underline a number in each set of brackets to make the sum correct.

47–49 $(11, 9, 5) \times (4, 7, 6) = (54, 55, 56)$

50–52 $(14, 11, 13) - (8, 7, 5) = (10, 8, 2)$

Underline the pair of words which do not have similar meanings.

53	behaviour/conduct	disease/sickness	many/few
54	level/even	latitude/longitude	hide/conceal
55	initial/final	avoid/elude	clasp/hug
56	ally/helper	asleep/awake	last/end
57	bad/evil	decrease/reduce	ebb/flow
58	force/compel	live/die	loose/release
59	prose/verse	lasting/durable	enemy/foe

Write a word in the space which satisfies the definition, and which rhymes with the word on the left.

60 see   A place where ships are unloaded   ....

61 dim   We sing this at church and at school   ....

62 rout   A shortage of rain   ....

63 him   A part of the body   ....

64 how   A part of a tree   ....

65 home   We use this to tidy our hair   ....

66 mist   Part of an arm   ....

67 How many minutes are there in a Thursday?   ....

One word can be used for each pair of definitions.

68 Frozen rain
To call from afar (....................)

69 Grumble
A game bird (....................)

70 A spike of corn
Part of the head (....................)

71 Healthy
Oil is obtained from one (....................)

72 A season
To leap (....................)

73 A locomotive
To instruct (....................)

74 We stick it on a letter
To tread heavily (....................)

Fill in the missing figures in the following sums.

75–78
```
   2 7 4 5
   3 . . . 4 . . . .
 + . . . . 8 . . . 7
 ─────────
   9 2 6 1
```

79–81
```
   . . . . . . 3 5
 ×   . . . .
 ─────────
   6 8 1 0
```

82–85
```
   3 . . . 5 . . . .
 ×         9
 ─────────
   2 . . . 4 . . . 3
```

Here is part of a chronological table.

BC
100 Julius Caesar is born
61   Julius Caesar became Governor of Spain
58   Julius Caesar invaded Britain
45   Julius Caesar is given supreme power in Rome
44   Julius Caesar is murdered by Brutus and others
43   Cleopatra became queen of Egypt

86 How old was Julius Caesar when he became Governor of Spain? .... years

87 How old was Julius Caesar when he invaded Britain? .... years

88 How old was he when he became the ruler in Rome? .... years

89 What was his age when he died? .... years

90 How long after Caesar's death did Cleopatra become queen of Egypt? .... year

91 For how many years did Caesar live after he invaded Britain? .... years

92 If Emperor Augustus died in AD14 how long was this after the death of Caesar? .... years

10% is another way of saying $\frac{1}{10}$, so 20% must be $\frac{2}{10}$ or $\frac{1}{5}$.
Find 20% of:

93 45   94 30   95 60   96 75   97 £5·50

....

46

Telephoning in an emergency

1 Call the operator by dialling 999.

2 Tell the operator which service you want: Fire, Police or Ambulance.

3 Wait until the Emergency Service answers.

4 Give the full address of the place where help is needed and any other information they ask for.

98 You should (tell the operator where help is needed, tell her which of the services you need, dial the number she gives you)

99 In the telephone directory you are told how to dial 999 without looking at the numbers. This is (because it is clever to do this, because it is easier to do it without looking, in case you have to do it in the dark)

100 When the Emergency Service answers you should (give them your name, tell them where you want help, tell them how the accident happened)

Paper 10

From the letters of the word **prosperous**, form words with the given meanings. Use each letter once only.

1 Correct ....
2 Riders use these ....
3 Part of a meal ....
4 We keep money in it ....
5 To go against ....
6 An old-fashioned name for a husband or wife ....

Find the two letters which will best end the first word and start the second word.

7 purp........ague   8 mosa........icle
9 bran........arge   10 plur........most
11 peri........ield   12 fast........gine

Underline the correct definition.

13 At the eleventh hour
At the darkest time of night
To go to bed late
At the last moment
Too late to be any good

14 To split hairs
To comb out tangles in one's hair
To argue over trifles
To have one's hair cut
To make a cutting remark

15 If we reduced the number of minutes in an hour to 40 how many hours would there be in a day? ....

Choose the right word from the list on the right to fill each space.

father	young	
16 swan	....	fawn
17 hare	....	cub
18 stallion	....	cygnet
19 gander	....	kid
20 stag	....	leveret
21 goat	....	foal
22 bear	....	gosling

House of Plantaganet	Reign
Henry II	1154–1189
Richard I	1189–1199
John	1199–1216
Henry III	1216–1272
Edward I	1272–1307
Edward II	1307–1327
Edward III	1327–1377
Richard II	1377–1399

23 Which of these kings reigned for the longest time? ....

24 Which king reigned for the shortest time? ....

25 For how long did the Plantaganets reign? ....

26 Which king was ruling England at the beginning of the thirteenth century? ....

27 The Black Death was in 1348 and 1349. Who was king then?
....

28 The Model Parliament met in 1295. Who was king then?

....

29 Who was on the throne at the beginning of the fourteenth century?
....

Can you think of a word which can be put in front of the other words on the line to form a compound word or a phrase?

30	bar	jug	maid	chocolate	....
31	master	light	dress	quarters	....
32	paste	ache	brush	powder	....
33	writing	kerchief	shake	cuff	....
34	nail	tip	print	mark	....
35	ball	path	step	print	....

Complete the following proverbs by using a word from the column on the right-hand side of the page.

36 .... is the best policy.   success

37 Many .... make light work.   birds

38 Nothing succeeds like ....   hay

39 Practice makes ....   lining

40 Make .... while the sun shines.   honesty

41 Every cloud has a silver ....   action

42 Spare the rod and spoil the ....   perfect

43 Kill two .... with one stone.   hands

44 .... speaks louder than words.   child

49

The first word in each line can be changed into the second word in three stages, by altering one letter at a time. Fill in the gaps.

45–46	wide	....	....	sing
47–48	hoot	....	....	boar
49–50	take	....	....	mine
51–52	hill	....	....	mole

Underline the word which is in some way different from the others.

53	call	summon	proclaim	cry	conceal	declare
54	durable	firm	weak	lasting	enduring	permanent
55	entire	complete	whole	part	intact	unbroken
56	enemy	foe	adversary	opponent	antagonist	colleague
57	singular	strange	plural	odd	peculiar	unique

If a statement is true write **t** in the space; if it is false write **f**.

58 Five 50p pieces have the same value as twenty-five 10p pieces.
....

59 December 26th is Christmas Day. ....

60 If January 14th is a Wednesday then the previous Thursday was January 7th. ....

61 If New Year's Day is on a Thursday the last day of January is a Saturday. ....

62 New York is the capital of the U.S.A. ....

63 April and September both have 31 days. ....

64 A decade is a period of 20 years. ....

Here is a list of the average daily hours of sunshine in Manchester. They are written very accurately. Can you write them to the nearest whole number of hours?

65	April	5·1	....
66	May	7·5	....
67	June	3·9	....
68	July	4·0	....
69	August	3·8	....
70	September	4·3	....
71	October	2·7	....

Here are the marks fifty children received in four tests.

Subject	Marks					
	0–29	30–44	45–54	55–64	65–74	75+
English	6	11	9	8	9	7
French	4	10	12	9	10	5
Mathematics	6	9	14	7	8	6
Science	8	12	11	8	7	4

72 How many children had fewer than 45 marks in Mathematics?
....

73 .... children had more than 54 marks in Science.

74 In French how many had between 30 and 64 marks? ....

75 .... children had more than 64 marks in English.

76 The biggest group in the under 45 marks set was in ....

Three people went to a Chinese restaurant and had the set menu. It was:

```
                    MENU
        Spring roll                    60p
        Sweet & sour chicken           £4.50
        Rice                           80p
        Honey & ginger ice cream       £1.30
        Coffee                         85p
```

77–84 Complete the bill for the three of them.

	£ p
Spring rolls	....
Chicken	....
Rice	....
Ice cream	....
Coffee	....
	....
10% service charge	....
	....

Mrs. Scott was born in 1942. Her daughter was born when she was 27, and her son was born three years previously.

85 In which year was Mrs. Scott's daughter born? ....

86 Her son was born in ....

87 How old will the son be when Mrs. Scott is 60? ....

Look at this map.

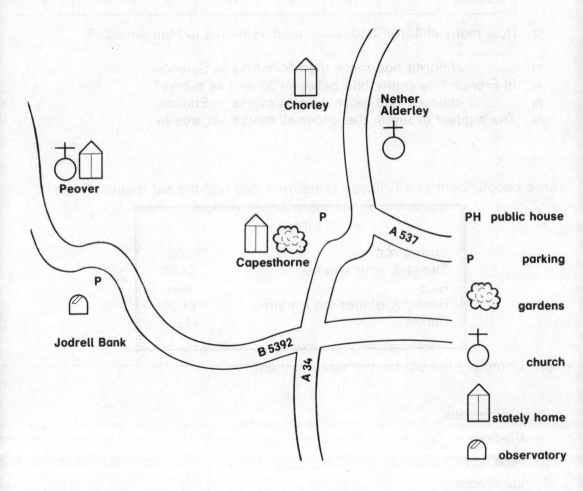

88 There are a stately home and a church in ....

89 There is just a stately home (no gardens to view) at ....

90 There is an observatory at ....

91 Capesthorne is on which road? ....

92 Jodrell Bank is on the ....

93 There is just a church at ....

This chart shows the distances between various cities.

	Dublin	Geneva	Madrid
London	449 km	753 km	1246 km
New York	5103 km	6201 km	5763 km
Paris	782 km	409 km	1054 km
Rome	1905 km	715 km	1358 km

94 How far is it from London to Madrid? ....

95 It is .... from Paris to Geneva.

96 The longest distance between two cities is
   from ....

97 The shortest distance is between ....

98 It is .... from Madrid to Paris.

99 Which is the longer distance? (Rome to Geneva, Paris to Dublin)

100 From Rome to Madrid is ....

Paper 11

Choose a word from the list on the right to fill each space.

1 Dad was very annoyed and it was difficult
   to .... him.

2 The lion catches and eats other animals; it is
   a .... creature.

3 Our car was stuck in a snowdrift. Should we
   wait for help to arrive or should we start
   walking? It was a ....

4 We decided to play football, a game in which we
   could all ....

5 A sponge soaks up water; it is made of
   a .... material.

6 Balanced on the handlebars of his bicycle, the
   clown was in a .... position.

7 He was knocked out in one of
   the .... rounds.

participate
predicament
precarious
porous
placate
preliminary
predatory

My watch is 8 minutes fast, and the bus which should have arrived at
4.32 p.m. is 6 minutes late.

8 What time does my watch show when the bus arrives? ....

Anne and Emma learn Spanish and French; Emma and Lucy learn French
and German. Caroline and Anne learn Welsh and Spanish.

9   Who learns French but not German? ....
10 Who learns Spanish but not Welsh? ....
11 Which language doesn't Anne learn? ....
12 Which language doesn't Emma learn? ....
13 How many of the girls learn three languages? ....

On each line there are two words which have similar meanings.
Underline these words.

14–15	walker	pedlar	scene	pedestrian	sight
16–17	full	vacant	let	empty	go
18–19	narrate	entice	design	investigate	recite

Write the following numbers in Roman numerals.

20 165   21 209
    ....

22 414   23 388
    ....

24 Two months of the year begin with the 13th letter of the alphabet. Write the second letter of the month that is between them. ....

Write a word which matches the definition, and which also rhymes with the word on the left.

25 poke   Part of an egg   ....
26 mat   An insect   ....
27 pile   Part of a church   ....
28 mains   Our blood travels in these ....
29 lane   Part of a bridle   ....

From the letters of the word **discriminate** form new words having the following meanings.

30 To cut into small pieces   ....
31 A packing case   ....
32 Boiling water produces this   ....
33 Digger of coal   ....
34 Wrong-doing often punished by imprisonment ....

35 If **deaf** contains the 6th letter of the alphabet write **x** unless **cadge** contains the 7th letter in which case write **z**. ....

Complete the following proverbs by choosing a word from the column on the right.

36 Where there's a will there's a ....   mile
37 When the cat's away the mice will ....   mind
38 There are two sides to every ....   robbery
39 Out of sight, out of ....   basket
40 A friend in need is a friend ....   way
41 A miss is as good as a ....   question
42 Don't put all your eggs in one ....   play
43 Fair exchange is no ....   indeed

One number in each line is wrong. Underline that number, and write the correct number in the space at the end of the line.

44	168	156	143	132	120	108	....
45	3	7	14	18	25	33	....
46	4	8	9	12	13	16	....
47	827	726	645	554	463	372	....
48	192	283	374	455	556	647	....
49	11	15	14	18	17	20	....

55

John's birthday is in the month after the month which starts with the 15th letter of the alphabet.

50 In which month was John born? ....

Use all the letters of each word on the left to form a new word with the given meaning.

51	present	A snake	....
52	ocean	A small boat	....
53	wolves	A part of the alphabet	....
54	drawer	Person in charge of prisoners	....
55	tutor	A fish	....
56	pastel	a fastener made of bent wire	....
57	trestle	Brought by the postman	....

One word on each line cannot be formed from the letters of the word on the left, using each letter once only. Underline that word.

58	**endorsement**	stored	deter	order	drone	storm
59	**parliament**	temper	plain	lament	ailment	trail
60	**deliverance**	clean	creed	anvil	driver	leader
61	**descendant**	scene	decant	scant	tended	tandem
62	**representative**	instep	interest	string	rest	entire
63	**conversation**	store	version	inverse	stance	scooter

Put these words into alphabetical order.
   furrow   fuse   further   fuss   furniture   fury   furnace

64 Which is the middle word? ....
65 Which is the last word? ....
66 Which is the first word? ....

67 Write the time which is 2 hours 50 minutes later than 10.35 p.m.
   ....

68 Write the time which is 3 hours 15 minutes earlier than 9.35 a.m.
   ....

On each line there is a sum which does not have the same answer as the sum in the left-hand column. Underline that sum.

69	$63 \div 7$	$(3 \times 3 \times 1)$	$(4 \times 2) + 1$	$(5 \times 2) \times 1$
70	$84 \div 12$	$(1 + 2 + 4)$	$(3 \times 3) - 1$	$(4 \times 2) - 1$
71	$108 \div 9$	$(3 \times 4) + 1$	$(11 \times 1) + 1$	$(2 \times 7) - 2$
72	$121 \div 11$	$(3 \times 3) + 2$	$(100 \div 10) - 1$	$(2 \times 4) + 3$
73	$56 \div 7$	$(64 \div 8)$	$(40 \div 5)$	$(28 \div 4)$

Here are some counties of England, with their county towns, areas and populations.

County	County town	Area in km	Population
Avon	Bristol	1346	920 000
Cheshire	Chester	2328	930 000
Norfolk	Norwich	5335	690 000
Suffolk	Ipswich	3807	602 000
Merseyside	Liverpool	646	1 521 000
Cornwall	Truro	3546	422 000

74 Which is the county town of the county with the smallest area?
....

75 Which is the county town of the county with the largest area?
....

76 Which is the county town of the county with the smallest population?
....

77 Which county has the largest population?   ....

78 The area of Suffolk is   ....

79–80 Which two counties have a difference of 10 000 in their populations?
....

Here is a chart which shows the number of people who stayed at Hillside Youth Hostel last year.

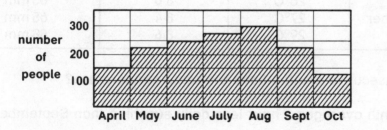

81 In which month did twice as many people stay there as in October?
....

82 In which month did half as many people stay there as in August?
....

83 The April and October figures put together were the same as those for
....

84 How many more people stayed there in August than in September?
....

85 How many fewer were there in May than in July?   ....

86 How many fewer than 2000 stayed there altogether?   ....

Type of call and charge band	Cheap rate Mon-Fri 6pm-8am All weekend			Standard rate Mon-Fri 8am-9am and 1pm-6pm			Peak rate Mon-Fri 9am-1pm		
	1 min	3 mins	5 mins	1 min	3 mins	5 mins	1 min	3 mins	5 mins
Local calls (L)	5p	5p	10p	5p	15p	20p	10p	20p	30p

Find the cost of:

87 A 3-minute call at 9 p.m. on Monday ....

88 A 5-minute call at noon on Wednesday ....

89 A 3-minute call at 8.30 a.m. on Tuesday ....

90 A 5-minute call at 11 a.m. on Sunday ....

91 How much do you save by making a 5-minute call at
10 p.m. rather than at 10 a.m. on Thursday? ....

92 What is the cost of a 3-minute call at 3.30 p.m. on Friday? ....

Here are some details about the climate in Kenya.

	Average daily temperature	Average hours of sun (daily)	Average monthly rainfall
April	30°C	7·4	195 mm
May	28°C	6·6	320 mm
June	27°C	7·5	120 mm
July	26°C	7·0	90 mm
August	26°C	8·0	65 mm
September	27°C	8·4	65 mm
October	29°C	8·6	88 mm

93 Which consecutive months have the same temperature?
....

94 Which month averages I hour less daily sunshine than September?
....

95-96 Two other months have the same temperature. They are
....

97 If you like it sunny and dry the best month is
....

98 If you like it sunny and dry the worst month is ....

99 Which month has the least sunshine? ....

100 If I had spent 5p more on a book I would have spent a quarter of my
money. If the book cost 85p how much money did I have at first?
....

Paper 12

1 Mrs. Oldham was born in 1891 and died in 1956. Her daughter was born when Mrs. Oldham was 28.
How old was the daughter when Mrs. Oldham died? ....

Underline the correct meaning of the following expressions.

2 **To be on tenterhooks**
To be hanging up
To be very sore
To be in suspense
To be spoilt

3 **A month of Sundays**
A month in which there are five Sundays
A leap year
A month when one is supposed to go to church
An extremely long period

4 **To see daylight**
To understand
How you feel when you wake up
What a diver sees when he comes to the surface
To be colour blind

5 **To be caught red-handed**
To be caught when you've cut your hand
To be caught doing wrong
To be caught painting your nails
To be caught playing with fire

6 **To make one's mark**
To learn to write
To mark time
To do very well indeed
To be a nuisance

Write the next number in each line.

7	924	835	746	657	568	479	....
8	7	15	9	17	11	19	....
9	3	6	7	14	15	30	....
10	21	18	19	16	17	14	....
11	2	6	4	12	6	18	....
12	5	7	10	14	15	21	....
13	1	4	9	16	25	36	....

59

On the left of the page are some long words, and on the right there is a column of shorter words. Can you match them for meaning?

14	**deficiency** means	hide
15	**aptitude** means	enemy
16	**copious** means	explain
17	**opulent** means	lack
18	**taciturn** means	rich
19	**secrete** means	ability
20	**reverberate** means	chew
21	**elucidate** means	much
22	**masticate** means	silent
23	**adversary** means	echo

Two pairs of words on each line have opposite meanings. One pair have not. Underline that pair.

24	order/disorder	dense/condense	use/misuse
25	regular/irregular	honest/dishonest	pact/impact
26	firm/confirm	pure/impure	content/discontent
27	real/unreal	certain/uncertain	spire/conspire
28	correct/incorrect	come/income	sufficient/insufficient
29	deed/indeed	finite/infinite	visible/invisible
30	known/unknown	fence/defence	active/inactive

Fill in the missing letters in these sentences.

31	I have a s........t........l for my school books.
32-33	I am a shop. I have co........ers and sh........es.
34	I am a camera. I take ....oto........phs.
35	I am a barometer. I forecast the w........t........r.
36	I am a plumb-line. I tell if things are ve........i........al.

There is one word on each line which is somehow different from the others. Underline that word.

37	brays	purrs	trots	neighs	bleats
38	bind	fix	tether	loosen	join
39	cruel	strong	robust	sturdy	powerful
40	prowls	howls	frisks	flits	crawls
41	butter	yogurt	apple	cheese	cream
42	waddles	struts	flutters	hops	crows
43	howl	groan	moan	fight	grumble

Complete the following sums by filling in the missing figures.

44–46
$$\begin{array}{r} 3\ldots8\,1 \\ \ldots4\,6\,9 \\ +\ 1\,6\,7\,4 \\ \hline 7\,9\ldots4 \\ \hline \end{array}$$

47–49
$$\begin{array}{r} 4\ldots7 \\ \times\quad\ldots \\ \hline 3\,1\,9\,9 \\ \hline \end{array}$$

50–51
$$\begin{array}{r} 9\,7\ldots4 \\ -\ 2\,3\,8\,1 \\ \hline 7\ldots0\,3 \\ \hline \end{array}$$

Here are some similes. Underline the correct word to make them complete.

52 As alike as two   (flowers, trees, peas, books, nuts)
53 As crooked as a   (corkscrew, fork, top, lane, monkey)
54 As dry as   (towel, cloth, cleaning, sand, dust)
55 As heavy as   (tonne, lead, weight, coal, house)
56 As stubborn as a   (horse, donkey, elephant, mule, cat)
57 As happy as a   (bird, lark, robin, joke, baby)

In the space at the end of each line write the following letters.

58	**x** beside the largest number	234 275	....
59	**y** beside the smallest number	234 943	....
60	**z** beside the number which is a multiple of 3	234 141	....
61	**b** by the number divisible by 5	224 129	....
62	**t** by the multiple of 11	234 751	....
63	**c** by the number divisible by 7	224 936	....
64	**d** by the multiple of 4	234 934	....

Think of a word which can be put in front of the other words on the line to form a compound word or a phrase.

65	ground	thing	time	wright	....
66	car	woman	force	officer	....
67	pond	cake	monger	hook	....
68	gage	house	grocer	fly	....
69	shelf	shop	marker	worm	....

Fill in the missing numbers and letters in each line.

70	1b	3d	2c	....	3d	5f
71	2b9	3c8	4d7	....	6f5	7g4
72	ba	db	fc	....	je	lf
73	az3	by4	cx5	....	ev7	fu8
74	1b3	2c4	3d5	....	5f7	6g8
75	284	375	466	....	648	739
76	bc1	ef2	hi3	....	no5	qr6

Here are some more letters written in braille.

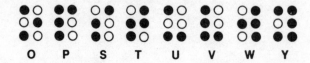

O   P   S   T   U   V   W   Y

What are these words?

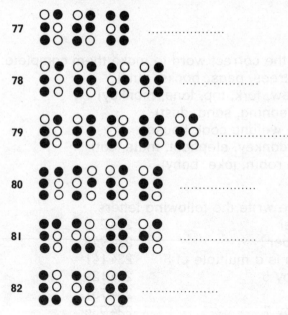

77 ....

78 ....

79 ....

80 ....

81 ....

82 ....

Here are some words written in a code, but they are mixed up. Can you sort them out?

cost	stale	least	beast
=@/−×	−×/=@	+×/=@	£÷=@

83 **cost** should be ....
84 **least** should be ....
85 **stale** should be ....
86 **beast** should be ....

In the same code, what are these words?

87 £/ = @ − × is   ....
88 + ÷ @@ − × is   ....
89 £ − ÷ = × = is   ....
90 £ ÷ + + − × is   ....

91–98 Can you work out what these jumbled words are?

Baked jacket potatoes

Burcs .... the potatoes, dry and **kricp** .... well with a
fork. **Shrub** .... with melted butter. **Cleap** .... on a
baking tray. **Kabe** .... till soft. When cooked cut in

flah .... and scoop out the potato. **Sham** .... well with
butter and seasoning. Replace filling and **verse** .... at once.

99 Mr. X takes 2 hours 30 minutes to do a journey at an average speed of
40 m.p.h. How far does he go?   ....
100 Mr. Y. does the same journey in 2 hours. What is his average speed?
....

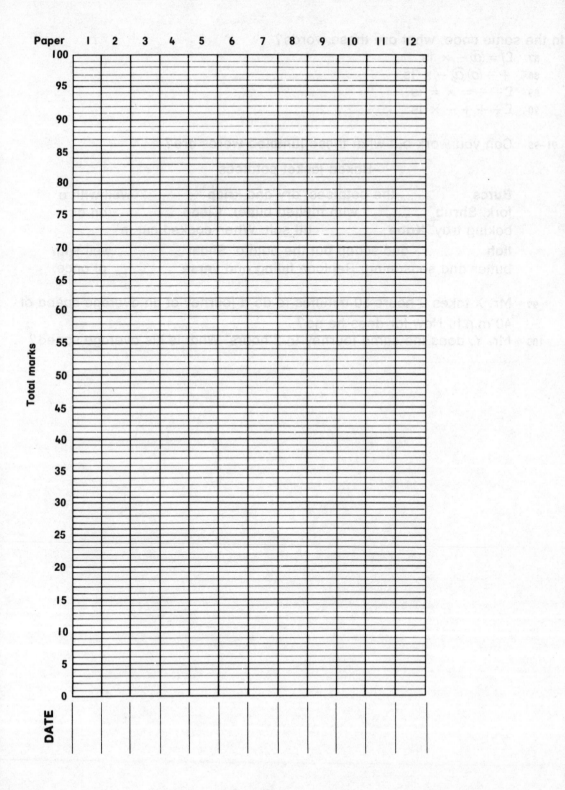

Total marks

Paper 1 2 3 4 5 6 7 8 9 10 11 12

100
95
90
85
80
75
70
65
60
55
50
45
40
35
30
25
20
15
10
5
0

DATE